FINGERPICKING

pop hits

HAL LEONARD EUROPE
Distributed by Music Sales

Exclusive Distributors:
Music Sales Limited
14–15 Berners Street, London W1T 3LJ, UK.

Order No. HLE90002682
ISBN 13: 978-1-84609-354-8
This book © Copyright 2007 Hal Leonard Europe

Cover design by Fresh Lemon
Printed in the USA

www.musicsales.com

INTRODUCTION TO FINGERSTYLE GUITAR

Fingerstyle (a.k.a. fingerpicking) is a guitar technique that means you literally pick the strings with your right-hand fingers and thumb. This contrasts with the conventional technique of strumming and playing single notes with a pick (a.k.a. flatpicking). For fingerpicking, you can use any type of guitar: acoustic steel-string, nylon-string classical, or electric.

THE RIGHT HAND

The most common right-hand position is shown below:

Use a high wrist; arch your palm as if you were holding a ping-pong ball. Keep the thumb outside and away from the fingers, and let the fingers do the work rather than lifting your whole hand.

The thumb generally plucks the bottom strings with downstrokes on the left side of the thumb and thumbnail. The other fingers pluck the higher strings using upstokes with the fleshy tip of the fingers and fingernails. The thumb and fingers should pluck one string per stroke and not brush over several strings.

Another picking option you may choose to use is called **hybrid picking** (a.k.a. plectrum-style fingerpicking). Here, the pick is usually held between the thumb and first finger, and the three remaining fingers are assigned to pluck the higher strings.

THE LEFT HAND

The left-hand fingers are numbered 1 though 4:

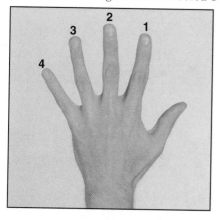

Be sure to keep your fingers arched, with each joint bent; if they flatten out across the strings, they will deaden the sound when you fingerpick. As a general rule, let the strings ring as long as possible when playing fingerstyle.

Band On The Run

Words and Music by Paul and Linda McCartney

Drop D tuning:
(low to high)D-A-D-G-B-E

Intro
Moderately slow

Bridge

If I ev - er get out ___ of here, thought of giv - ing it all ___ a - way

to a reg - is - tered char - i - ty. All I need is a pint ___ a day. If I

ev - er get out ___ of here. ___ (If we ev - er get out ___ of here.)

Interlude
Moderately fast

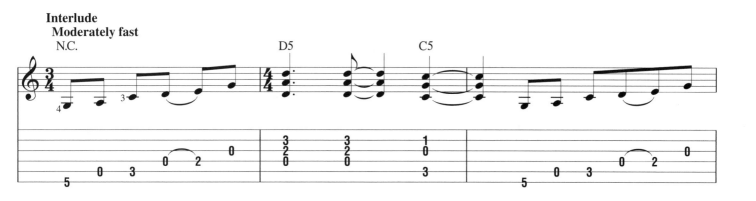

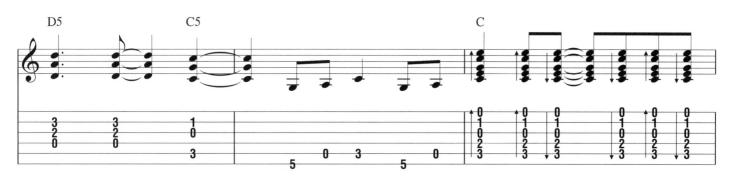

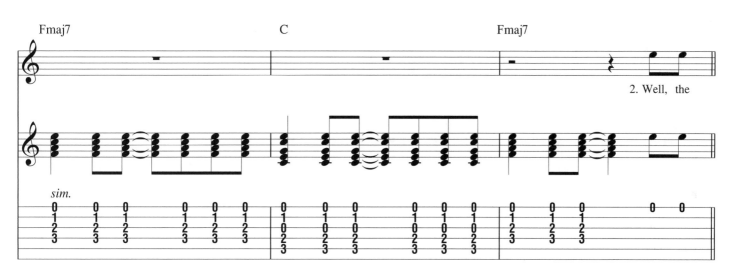

2. Well, the

Verse

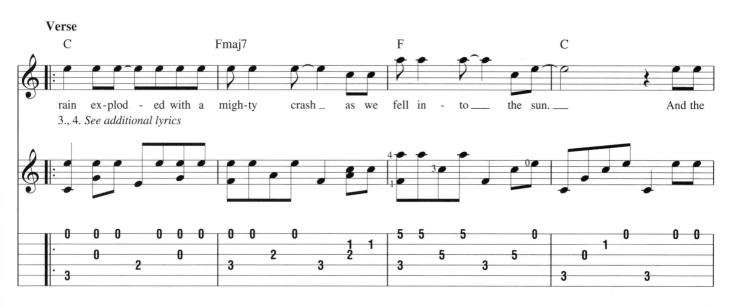

rain ex-plod - ed with a migh-ty crash ___ as we fell in - to ___ the sun. ___ And the

3., 4. *See additional lyrics*

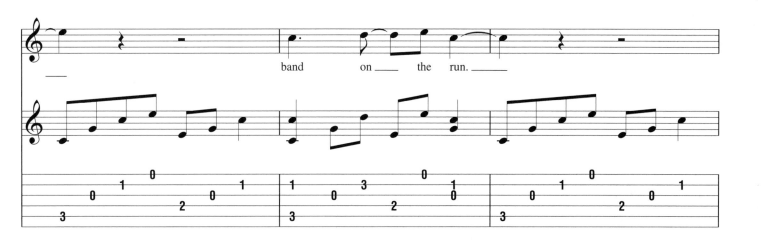

band   on _____ the   run. _____

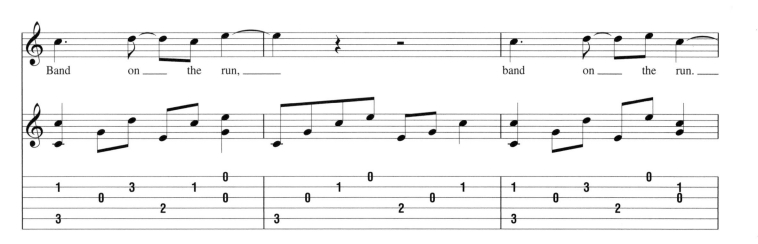

Band   on _____ the   run, _____   band   on _____ the   run. ____

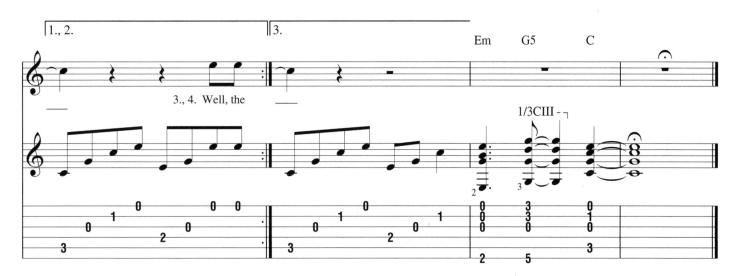

3., 4. Well, the _____

Additional Lyrics

3. Well, the undertaker drew a heavy sigh
Seeing no one else had come.
And a bell was ringing in the village square
For the rabbits on the run.

4. Well, the night was falling as the desert world
Began to settle down.
In the town, they're searching for us ev'rywhere
But we never will be found.

Bridge Over Troubled Water

Words and Music by Paul Simon

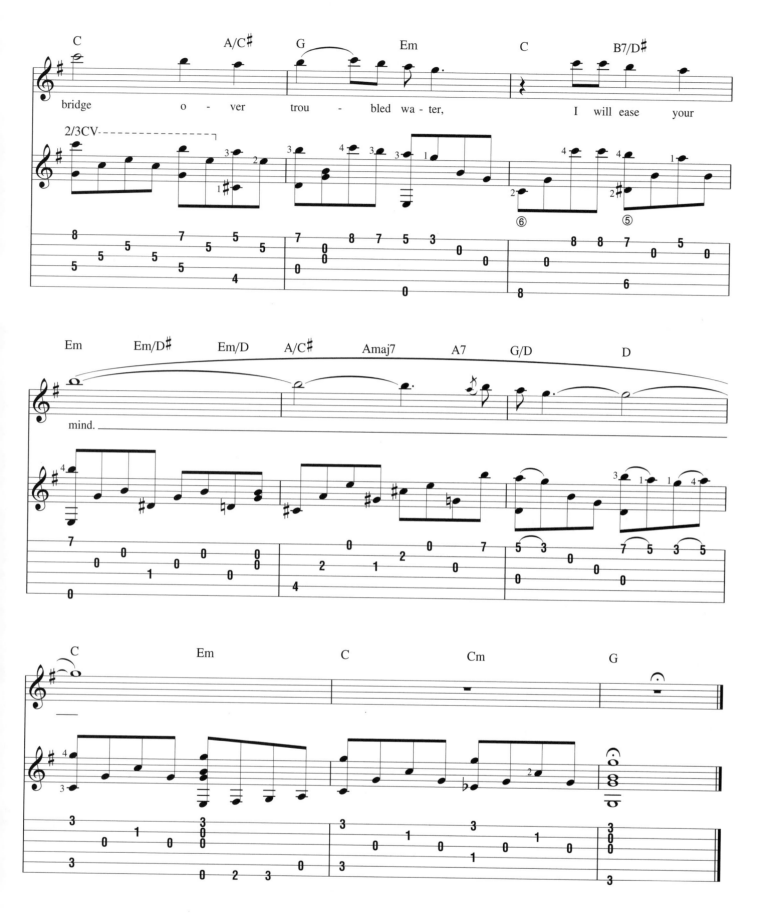

Additional Lyrics

2. When you're down and out, when you're on the street,
When evening falls so hard, I'll comfort you.
I'll take your part. Oh, when darkness comes and pain is all around,
Like a bridge over troubled water, I will lay me down.
Like a bridge over troubled water, I will lay me down.

Can You Feel The Love Tonight

from Walt Disney Pictures' THE LION KING

Music by Elton John
Lyrics by Tim Rice

1. There's a calm sur-ren-der to the rush of day when the heat of the roll-ing world
2. There's a time for ev'ry-one if they on-ly learn that the twist-ing ka-lei - do-scope

can be turned a - way. An en-chant-ed mo - ment, and it sees me through.
moves us all in turn. There's a rhyme and rea - son to the wild out - doors

It's e - nough for this rest - less war - ri - or just to be with you. And can you feel the love
when the heart of this star - crossed voy - ag - er beats in time with yours.

Chorus

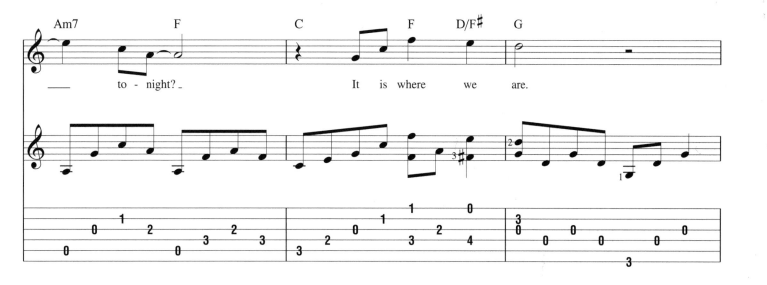

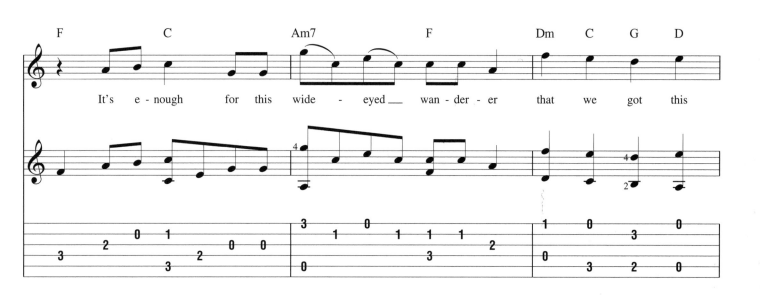

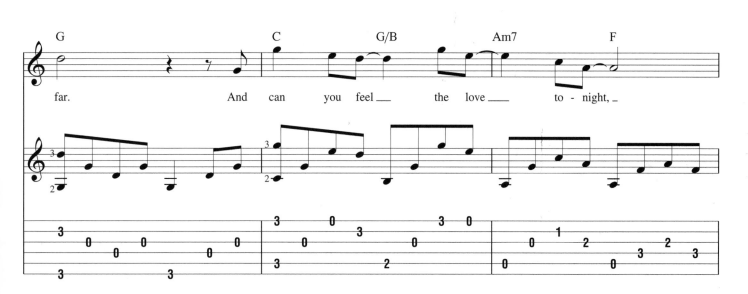

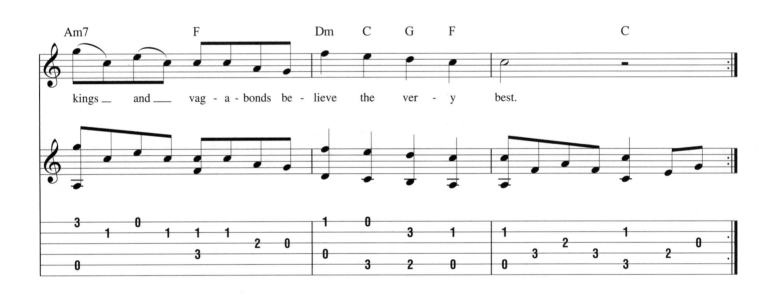

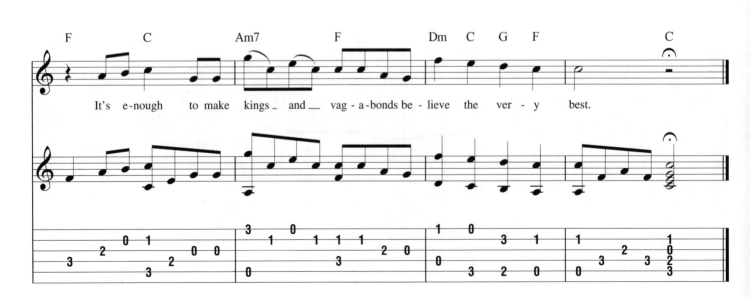

My Heart Will Go On

(Love Theme from 'Titanic')

from the Paramount and Twentieth Century Fox Motion Picture TITANIC

Music by James Horner
Lyric by Will Jennings

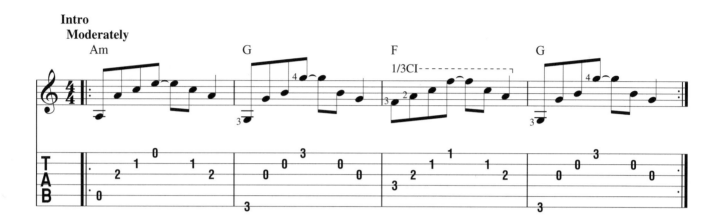

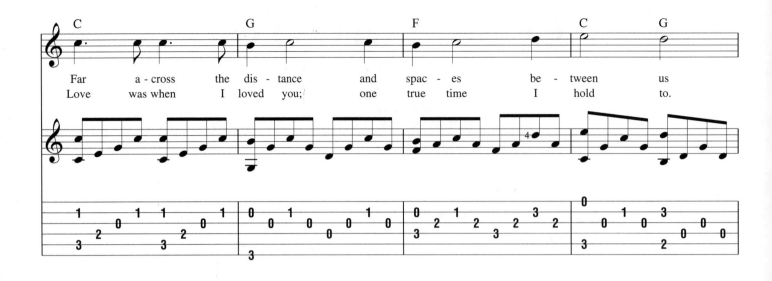

Far   a - cross   the   dis - tance   and   spac - es   be - tween   us
Love   was when   I   loved   you;   one   true   time   I   hold   to.

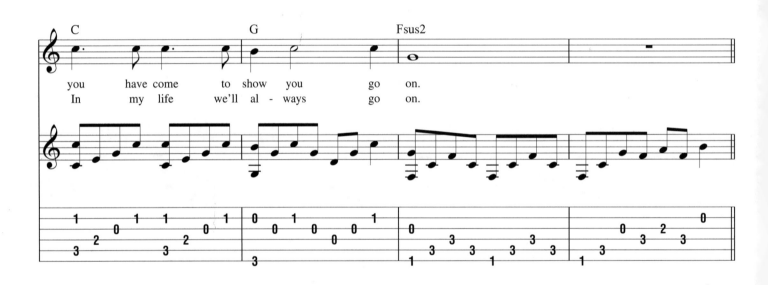

you   have come   to show   you   go   on.
In   my   life   we'll   al - ways   go   on.

Chorus

Near,   far,   wher - ev - er   you   are,   I   be -

lieve   that   the   heart   does   go   on. _____

Once   more   you   o - pen   the   door   and   you're

here   in   my   heart,   and   my   heart   will   go   on   and

We'll stay for - ev - er this

way. You are safe in my heart, and my heart will go

on and on.

Don't Know Much

Words and Music by Barry Mann, Cynthia Weil and Tom Snow

Drop D tuning:
(low to high) D-A-D-G-B-E

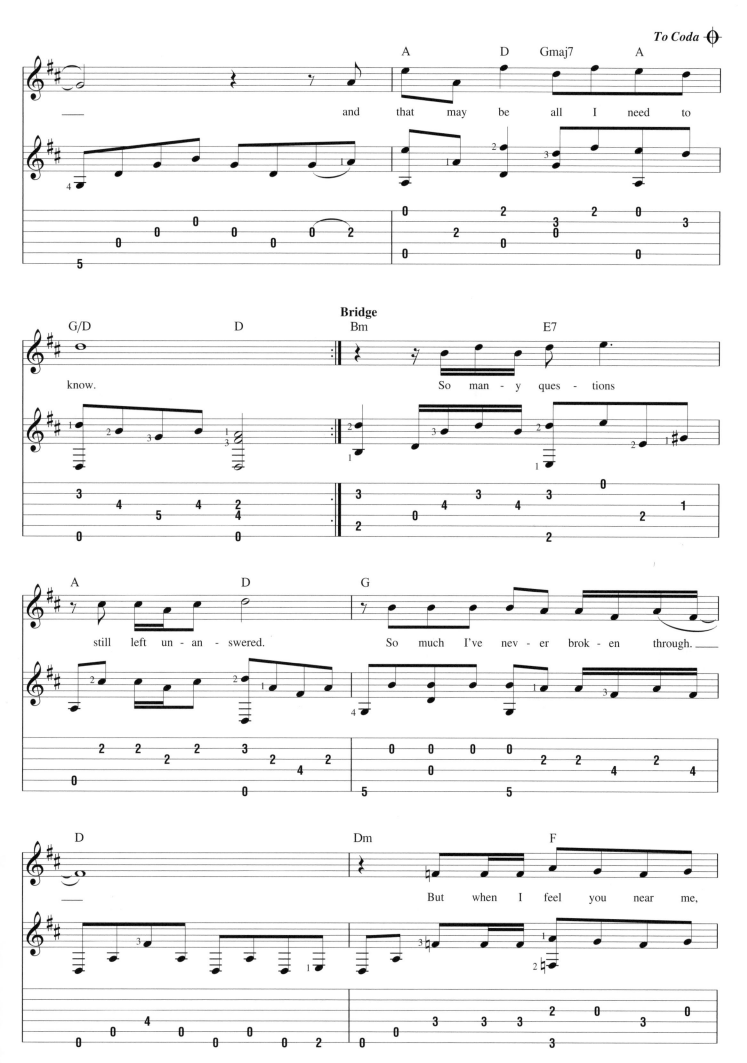

Coda

D. C. al Coda

Outro

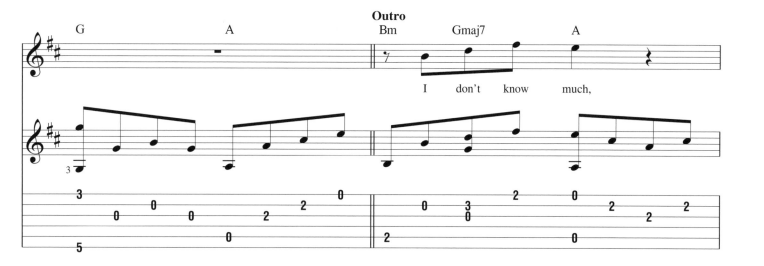

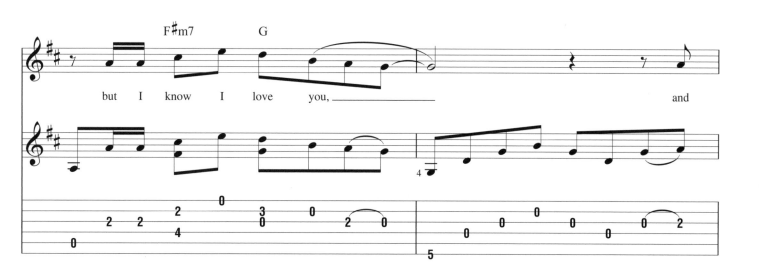

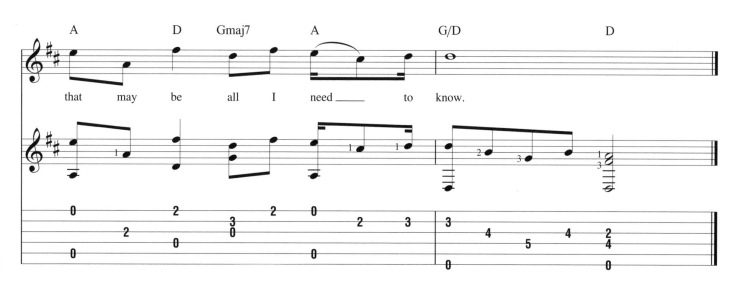

Additional Lyrics

2. Look at these eyes, they never seen what matters.
   Look at these dreams so beaten and so battered.
   I don't much, but I know I love you,
   And that may be all I need to know.

3. Look at this man so blessed with inspiration.
   Look at this soul still searching for salvation.
   I don't much, but I know I love you,
   And that may be all I need to know.

Don't Know Why

Words and Music by Jesse Harris

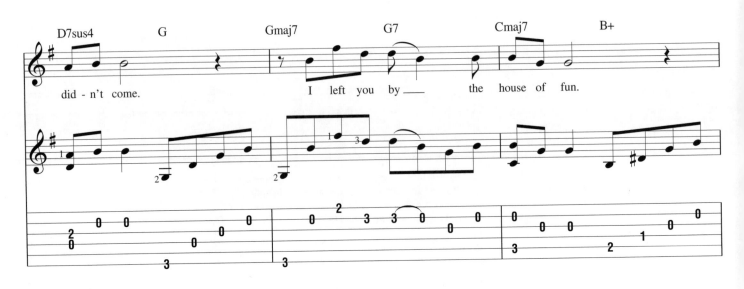

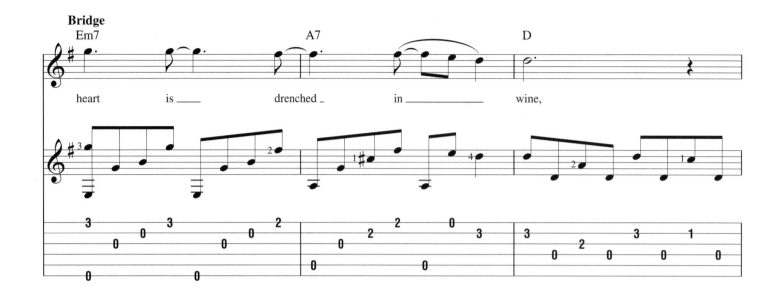

Bridge

heart   is ___   drenched _   in _____   wine,

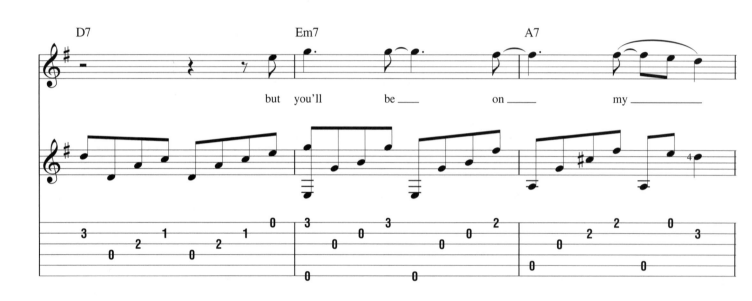

but   you'll   be ___   on ___   my _____

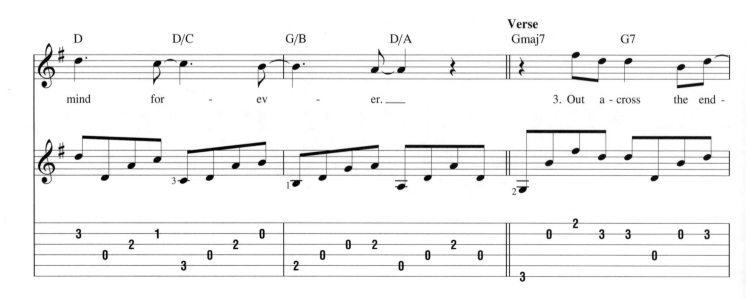

Verse

mind   for -   ev -   er. ___   3. Out   a - cross   the   end -

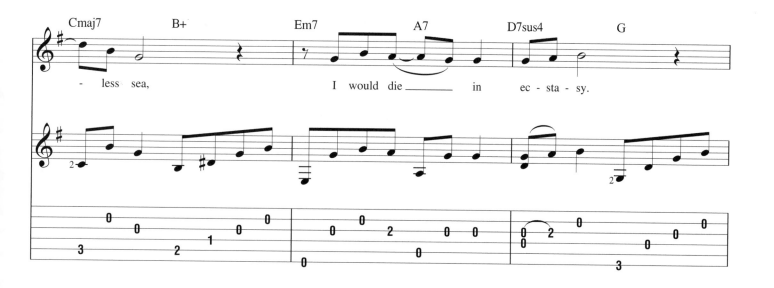

-less sea, I would die _____ in ec - sta - sy.

But I'll be _____ a bag _____ of bones driv - ing down _____ the road _

Bridge

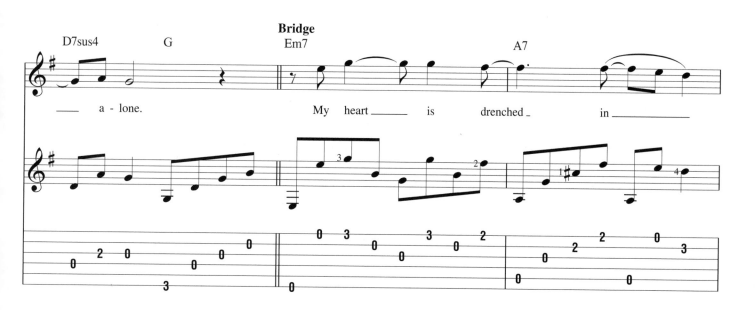

_____ a - lone. My heart _____ is drenched _ in _____

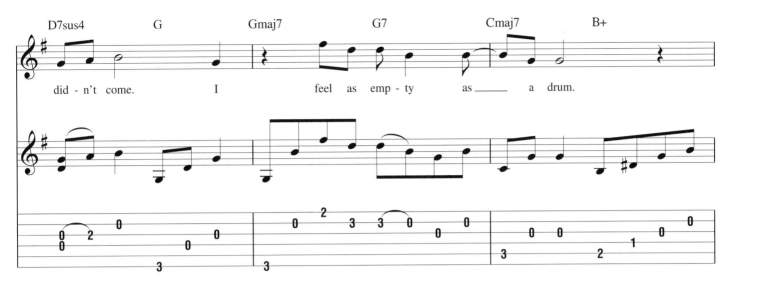

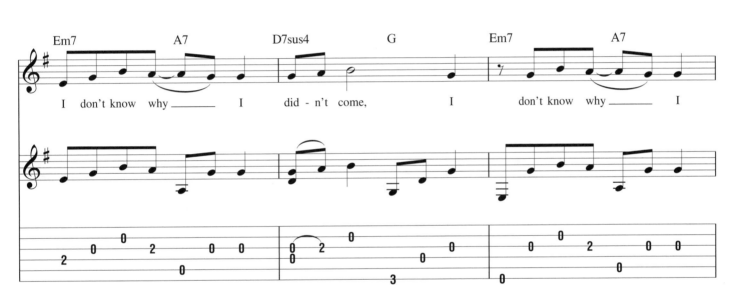

Every Breath You Take

Music and Lyrics by Sting

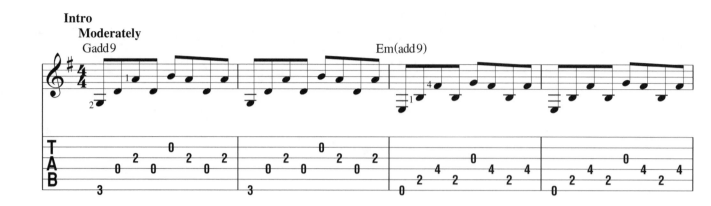

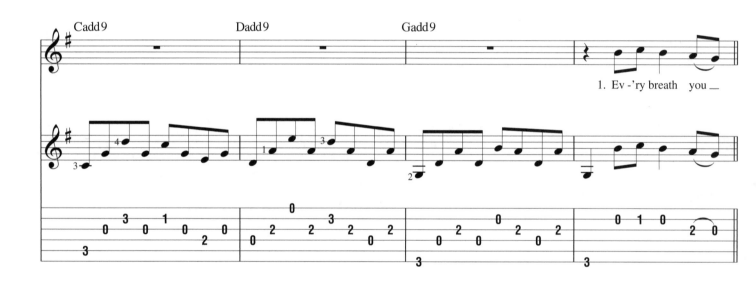

1. Ev -'ry breath you _

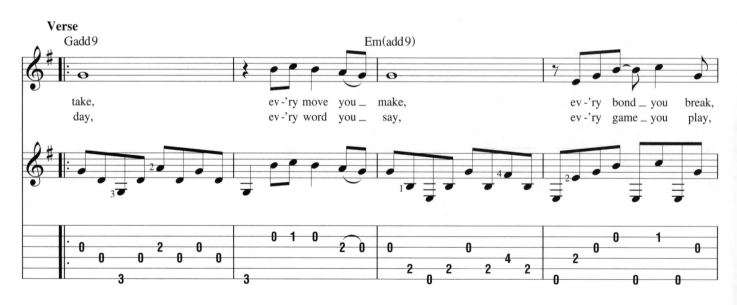

take,
day,
ev-'ry move you _ make,
ev-'ry word you _ say,
ev-'ry bond _ you break,
ev-'ry game _ you play,

Imagine

Words and Music by John Lennon

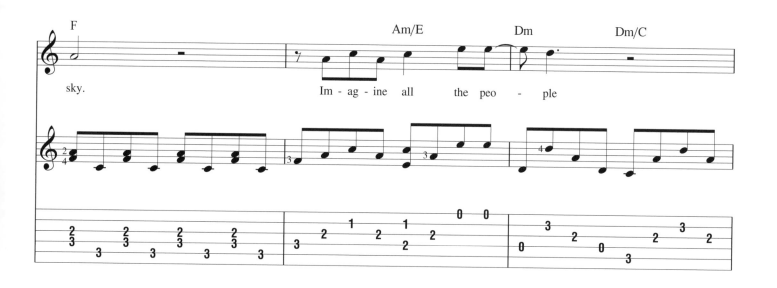

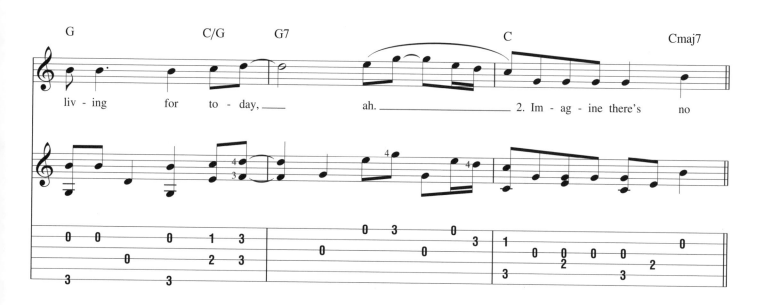

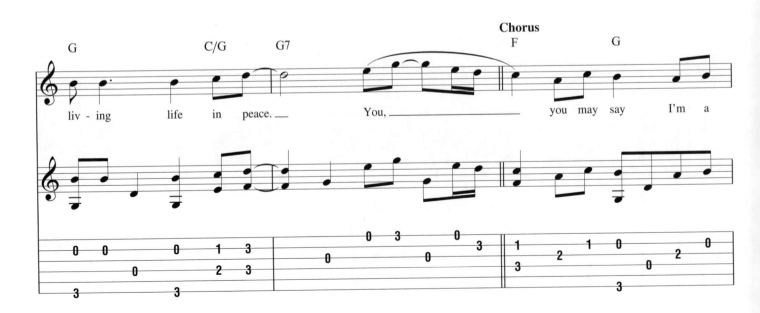

Additional Lyrics

3. Imagine no possessions,
I wonder if you can;
No need for greed or hunger,
A brotherhood of man.
Imagine all the people sharing all the world.

Let It Be

Words and Music by John Lennon and Paul McCartney

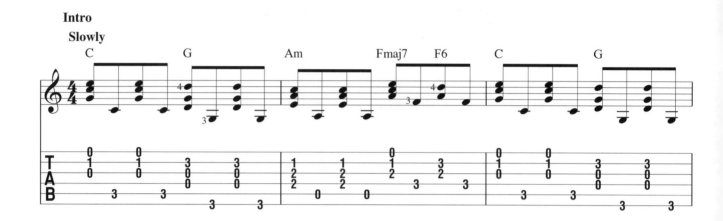

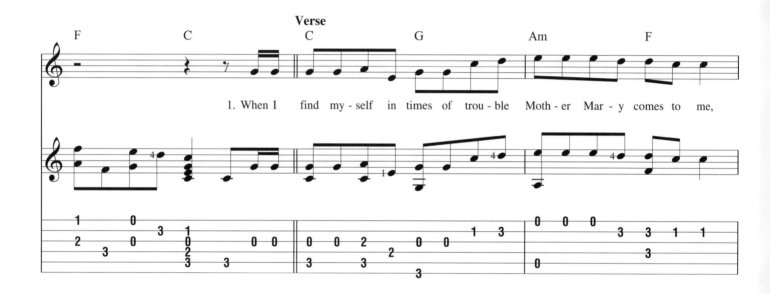

1. When I find my-self in times of trou-ble Moth-er Mar-y comes to me,

speak-ing words of wis-dom, ___ let it be. ___ And in my hour of dark-ness she is

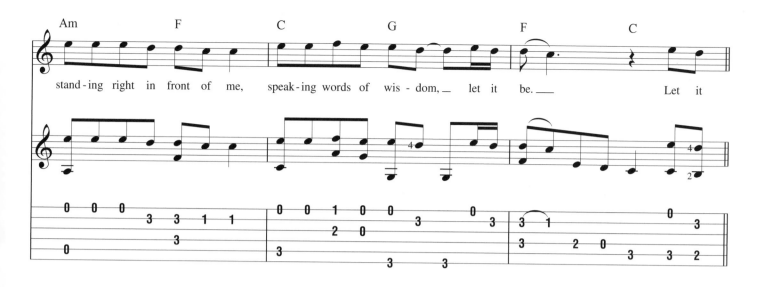

standing right in front of me, speaking words of wisdom, __ let it be. __ Let it

Chorus

be, let it be, __ let it be, __ let it be. Whisper words of wisdom, __ let it

Verse

be. __ 2. And when the broken-hearted people living in the world agree,
3. *See additional lyrics*

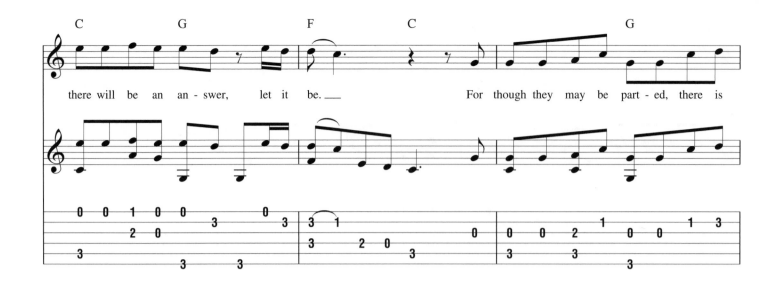

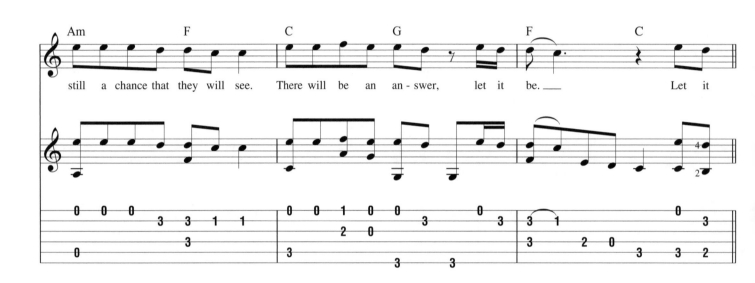

Chorus

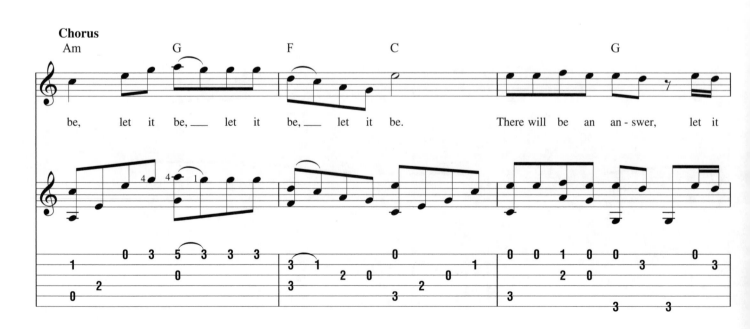

Additional Lyrics

3. And when the night is cloudy, there is still a light that shines on me,
   Shine until tomorrow, let it be.
   I wake up to the sound of music, Mother Mary comes to me,
   Speaking words of wisdom, let it be.

Sorry Seems To Be The Hardest Word

Words and Music by Elton John and Bernie Taupin

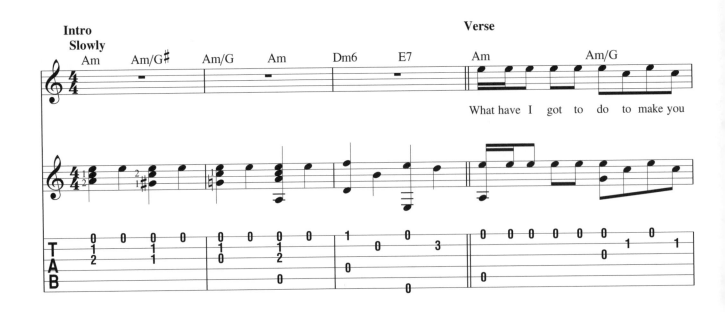

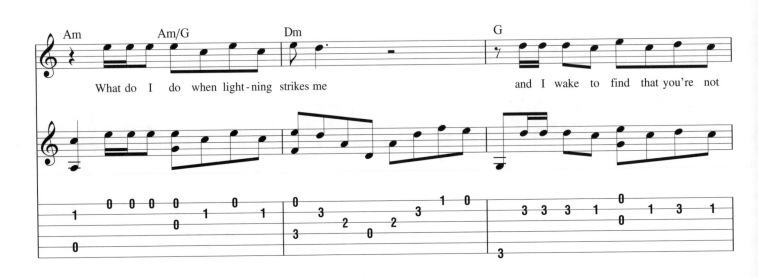

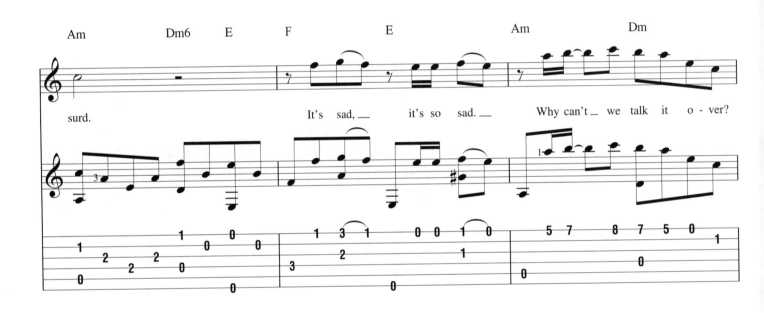

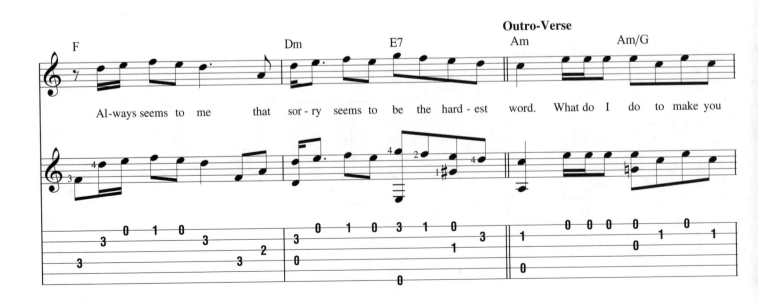

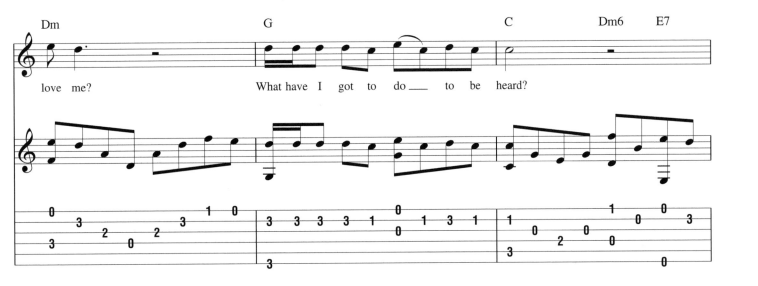

love me?   What have I got to do ___ to be heard?

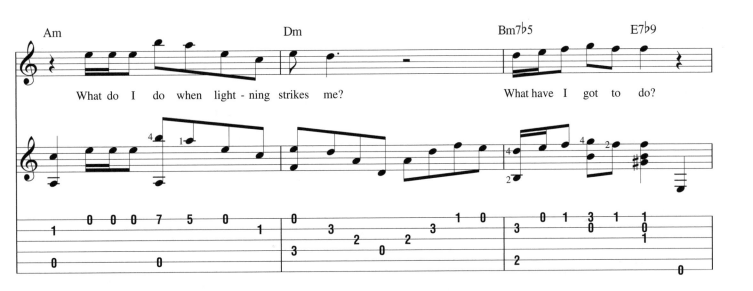

What do I do when light - ning strikes me?   What have I got to do?

What have I got to do? _____ Sor-ry seems to be the hard - est word. _____

Stand By Me

Words and Music by Ben E. King, Jerry Leiber and Mike Stoller

53

Wanted Dead Or Alive

Words and Music by Jon Bon Jovi and Richie Sambora

Drop D tuning:
(low to high) D–A–D–G–B–E

Intro
Moderately slow

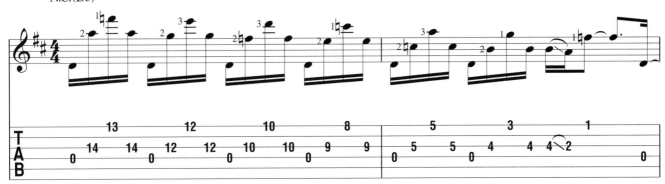

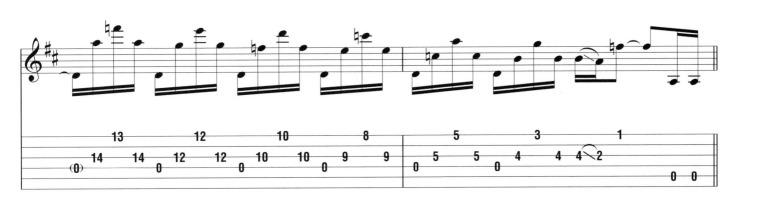

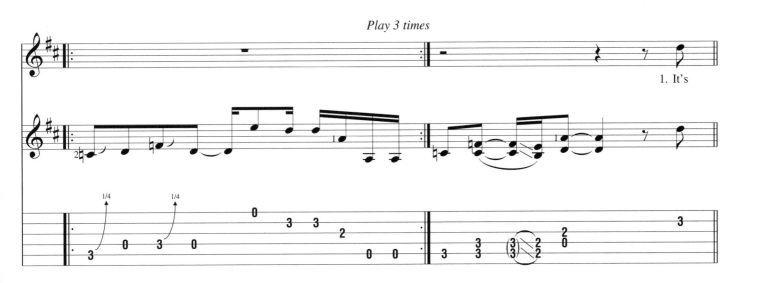

Outro

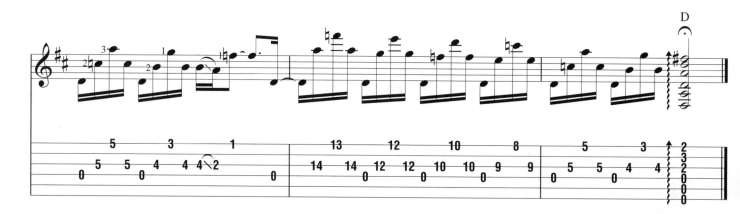

Additional Lyrics

2. Sometimes I sleep, sometimes it's not for days.
The people I meet always go their sep'rate ways.
Sometimes you tell the day by the bottle that you drink.
And times when you're alone, all you do is think.

3. And I walk these streets, a loaded six-string on my back.
I play for keeps, 'cause I might not make it back.
I been ev'rywhere, still I'm standing tall.
I've seen a million faces, and I've rocked them all.

We've Only Just Begun

Words and Music by Roger Nichols and Paul Williams

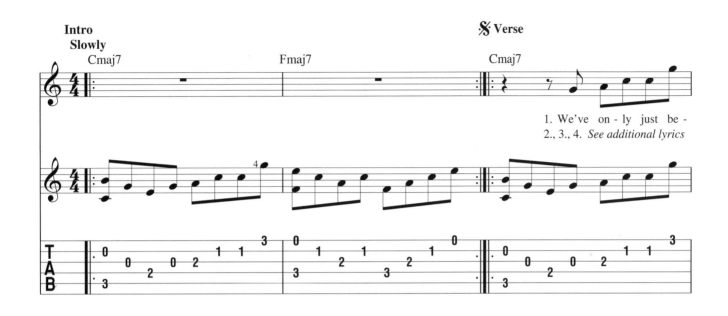

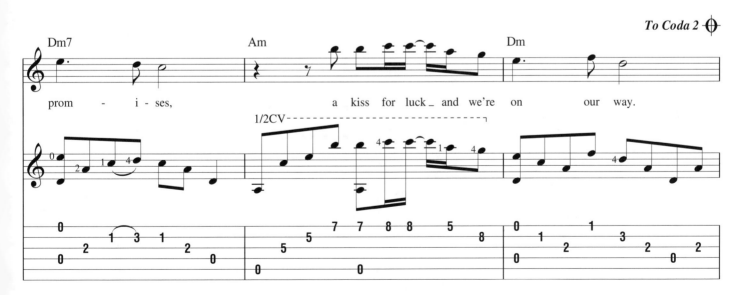

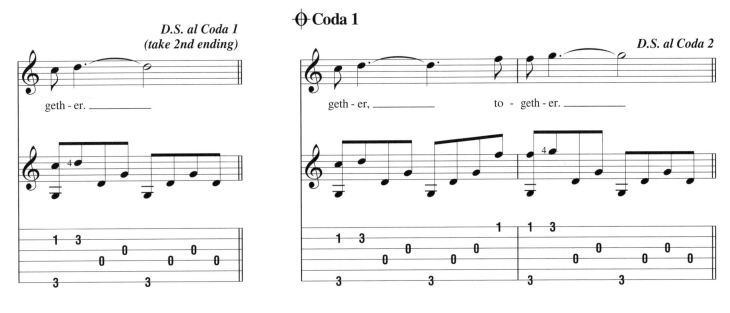

⊕ Coda 2

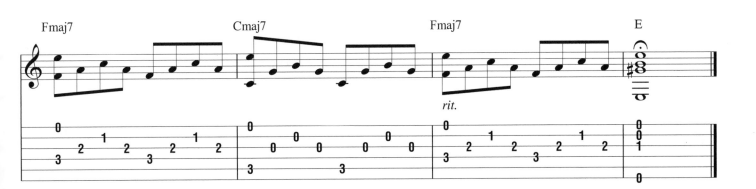

Additional Lyrics

2. Before the rising sun we fly,
   So many roads to choose,
   We start out walking and learn to run.
   And yes, we've just begun.

3., 4. And when the evening comes we smile,
   So much of life ahead,
   We'll find a place where there's room to grow.
   And yes, we've just begun.

Wonderful Tonight

Words and Music by Eric Clapton

1. It's late in the eve-ning; she's won-d'ring what clothes to wear. _
2., 3. *See additional lyrics*

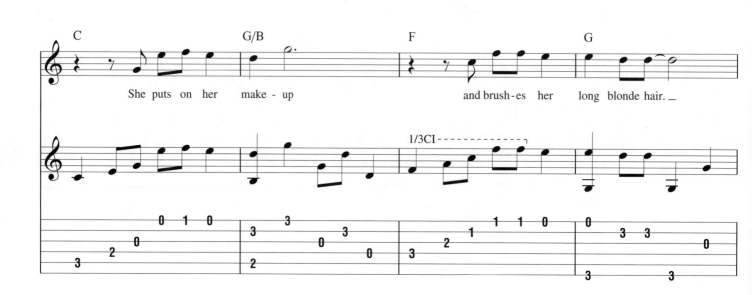

She puts on her make-up and brush-es her long blonde hair. _

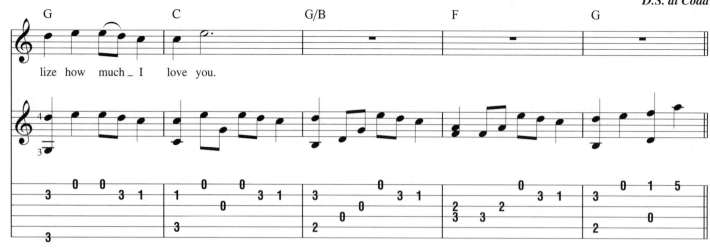

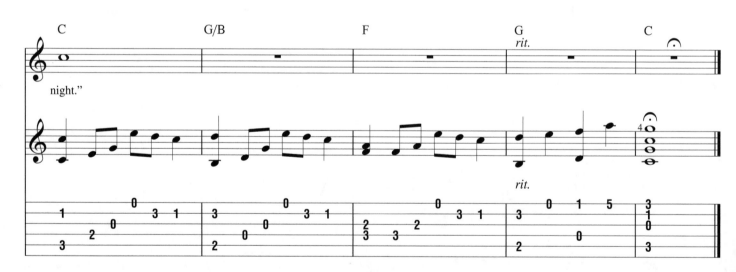

Additional Lyrics

2. We go to a party, and everyone turns to see
   This beautiful lady that's walking around with me.
   And then she asks me, "Do you feel all right?"
   And I say, "Yes, I feel wonderful tonight."

3. It's time to go home now, and I've got an aching head,
   So I give her the car keys; she helps me to bed.
   And then I tell her, as I turn out the light,
   I say, "My darlin', you were wonderful tonight.
   Oh, my darlin', you were wonderful tonight."

You'll Be In My Heart

(Pop Version)

from Walt Disney Pictures' TARZAN™

Words and Music by Phil Collins

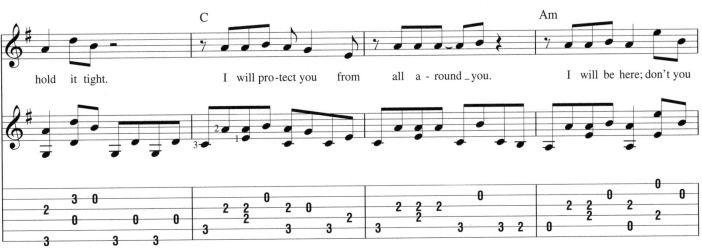

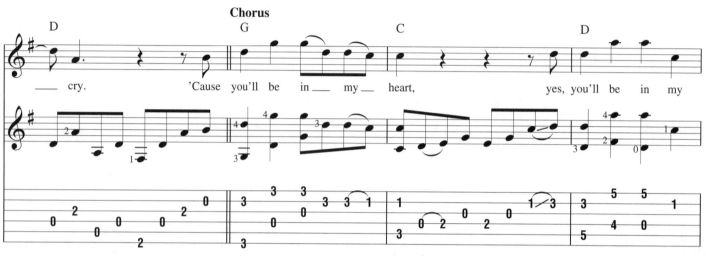

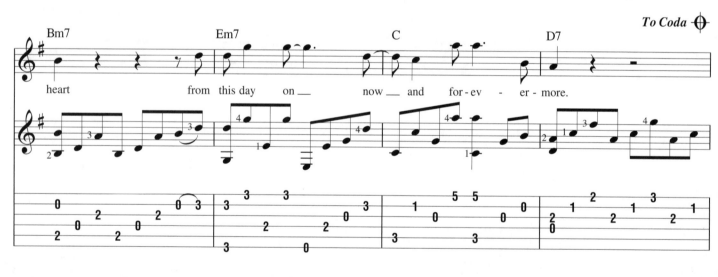

show them to-geth-er. 'Cause you'll be in ___ my ___ heart. Be-lieve me, you'll be in ___ my ___

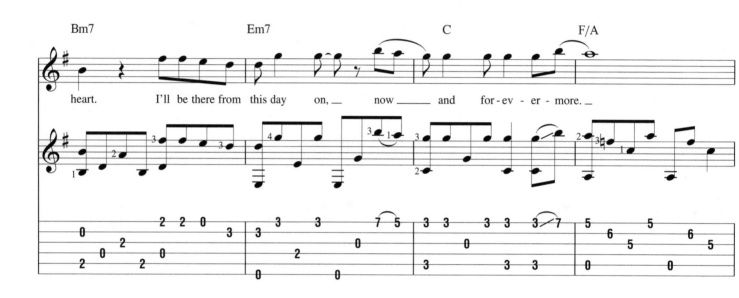

heart. I'll be there from this day on, ___ now ___ and for-ev-er-more. ___

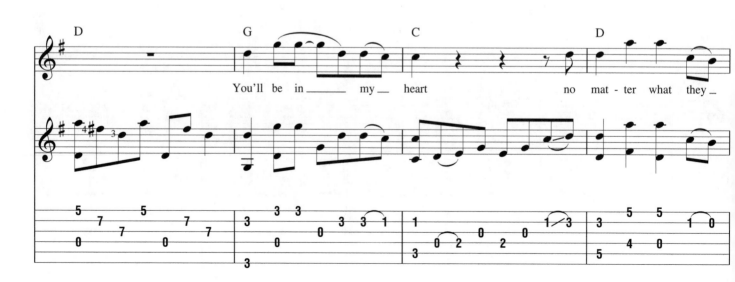

You'll be in ___ my ___ heart no mat-ter what they ___

70

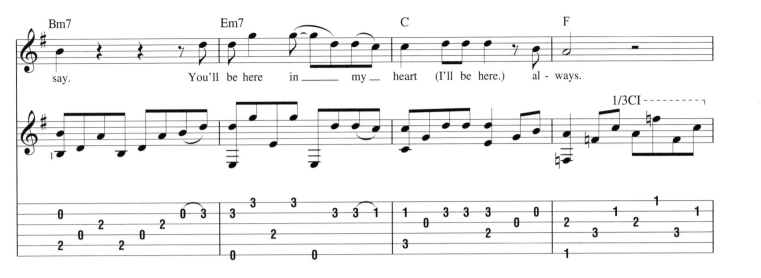

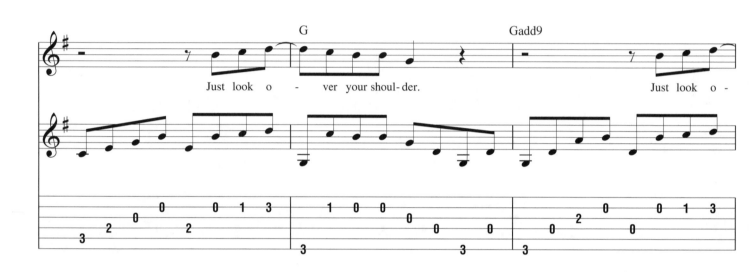

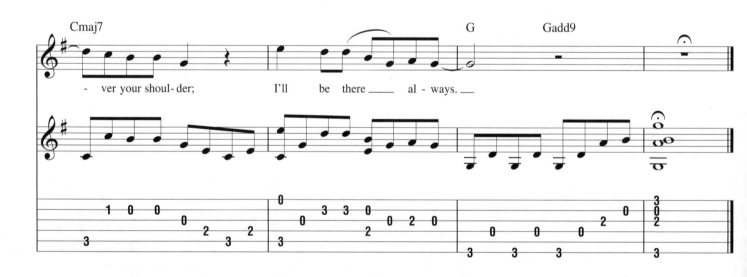

Additional Lyrics

2. Why can't they understand the way we feel?
They just don't trust what they can't explain.
I know we're diff'rent but deep inside us
We're not that different at all.
And you'll be in my heart...

Bridge When destiny calls you, you must be strong.
I may not be with you, but you've got to hold on.
They'll see in time, I know.